PRENTICE HALL
WRITING AND GRAMMAR

Daily Language Practice
Blackline Masters

Grade Six

PEARSON

Prentice
Hall

Boston, Massachusetts,
Upper Saddle River, New Jersey

ISBN 0-13-361711-4

1 2 3 4 5 6 7 8 9 10   10 09 08 07 06

Contents

Introduction to Daily Language Practice

A Tool for Success

The middle and high school years are a crucial period for the development of students' skills in all of the language arts. As a result, students need programs that provide individual and cooperative practice in reading, writing, speaking, and listening skills.

Prentice Hall's *Daily Language Practice* offers just such a framework for meaningful language arts practice. While focusing on grammar, mechanics, and usage skills, the program provides a fresh point of departure from the tedious, time-consuming drills of the past. Using *Daily Language Practice* for just a few minutes a day helps you provide your students with meaningful routines that ensure continuous progress. In effect, *Daily Language Practice* offers you a full toolbox for developing reading, writing, listening, and speaking skills.

Design and Organization

The basic components of language use—reading, writing, speaking, and listening—cannot be learned in isolation from each other. Rather, students learn best when all the language arts are integrated through authentic activities. Literature provides a natural context for practice in all of the language arts and is a natural springboard for teaching the full array of skills. The *Daily Language Practice* lessons are a logical outgrowth of this concept. Each lesson is tied to some aspect of the literature. Some lessons are keyed to specific literature selections, while others relate to literary genres, authors, themes, cross-curricular topics, or cross-cultural issues.

The literature used for *Daily Language Practice* topics reflects the best of the traditional and the contemporary… from time-honored classics to fresh voices. Short stories, drama, nonfiction, poetry, and novels are all incorporated. For example, the *Daily Language Practice* activities for the middle grades include sentences that relate to classics, such as Washington Irving's "Rip Van Winkle" and Lewis Carroll's "The Walrus and the Carpenter," as well as contemporary essays, such as "Barrio Boy" by Ernesto Galarza and "The Trouble with Television" by Robert MacNeil. There are exercises that discuss Caribbean culture, Kwanzaa, Greek myths, and American tall tales. What a natural, painless way for students to master the fundamentals of standard written English as they experience the rich literature of our varied culture!

Daily Language Practice lessons are organized in a series of thirty-six weeks. You may wish to start or end each language arts lesson with *Daily Language Practice*, or use the sentences as you work through lessons to integrate writing and grammar skills. The practice provides two sentences or passages a day, five days a week. This format allows you to provide your students with regular practice in language and writing skills. By spending five to ten minutes a day in revision and discussion, students will have a regular opportunity to improve their reading, writing, speaking, and listening skills.

By the way, some students may prefer to work on more than two sentences a day! Feel free to be flexible in your scheduling and to pace and work with the program in ways that are most beneficial to your students.

Making the Most of *Daily Language Practice*

We provide sentences in print and on overhead transparencies to facilitate your giving students a variety of options and presentations. Some of the different ways that you can guide your students through the *Daily Language Practice* include the following:

- Write the two Practice Sentences on the board every day. Students can work independently, in pairs, in small groups, or as a class to write and discuss the problems and corrections.
- Using the transparency, place the sentences on an overhead projector. Arrange students in learning groups to work through the sentences, discuss the problems, and make corrections.
- Dictate the sentences for students to write. Invite volunteers to isolate the errors and explain how to correct them.

As students listen, write, and discuss each sentence, they reinforce their listening, thinking, writing, and speaking skills. The combination of written and oral practice fully taps all learning modalities.

Daily Language Practice and Special Needs Populations

Daily Language Practice helps special needs populations by breaking down grammar, usage, and mechanics to its basic parts. ESL and LEP students are often overwhelmed by the sheer mass of information they must absorb. By providing only two, clear-cut passages a day, you can help your special needs students learn to learn in an effective, focused way.

Advantages and Outcomes

Daily Language Practice benefits all learners. Since the sentences build from simple to complex errors in each grade level, students gain confidence as they gain mastery. As they build to more complex skills, such as parallel structure and pronoun agreement, students gain a deeper understanding of the logic behind English structure. By the end of the thirty-six weeks of practice, students will have explored all the common errors in grammar, usage, and mechanics, and will have been presented with the knowledge they need to correct them!

Daily Language Practice

Daily Language Practice • Week 1

Day 1

Skills Practiced

Capitalization of a person's name.

Use of end punctuation: period.

Use of 's to show singular possession.

Practice Sentences

1. The main character in <u>The Sign of the Beaver</u> is matt
2. After he is stung by bees, Matts face swells.

Answers

1. The main character in <u>The Sign of the Beaver</u> is Matt.
2. After he is stung by bees, Matt's face swells.

Day 2

Skills Practiced

Use of comma after introductory word.

Use of commas to set off appositive.

Capitalization of proper adjective.

Practice Sentences

1. Awkwardly Matt tried to spear a fish.
2. Matt and Attean a native american boy became good friends.

Answers

1. Awkwardly, Matt tried to spear a fish.
2. Matt and Attean, a Native American boy, became good friends.

Day 3

Skills Practiced

Use of comma after mild interjection.

Correction of commonly confused words.

Combining sentence parts.

Practice Sentences

1. "Gee I wish Dad would get home soon," thought Matt.
2. Attean learned Matt to fish. Attean learned Matt to hunt.

Answers

1. "Gee, I wish Dad would get home soon," thought Matt.
2. Attean taught Matt to fish and hunt.

Day 4

Skills Practiced

Use of underlining or italics with foreign words.

Capitalization of first word of a sentence.

Practice Sentences

1. Seba, which means "tomorrow," is a word Matt learned from Attean.
2. Attean pointed to a tree and said, "Do you see this tree? it is marked with the sign of the beaver."

Answers

1. <u>Seba</u>, which means "tomorrow," is a word Matt learned from Attean.
2. Attean pointed to a tree and said, "Do you see this tree? It is marked with the sign of the beaver."

Day 5

Skills Practiced

Use of comma before coordinating conjunction in a compound sentence.

Use of apostrophe in a contraction.

Correction of sentence fragment.

Practice Sentences

1. Matt was tired but he didnt give up hope.
2. Matt cooked his meat over an open fire. Before the snow began to fall.

Answers

1. Matt was tired, but he didn't give up hope.
2. Matt cooked his meat over an open fire before the snow began to fall.

Daily Language Practice • Week 2

Day 1

Skills Practiced

Spelling out numbers under one hundred.

Revision of stringy sentence.

Formation of irregular plural.

Practice Sentences

1. The caravan across the wilderness was small and consisted of only 5 wagons and each wagon was pulled by a team of animals.
2. To start the wagons, Hank signaled the oxes.

Answers

1. The caravan across the wilderness was small. It consisted of only five wagons. Each wagon was pulled by one team of animals.
2. To start the wagons, Hank signaled the oxen.

Day 2

Skills Practiced

Correct use of indefinite article.

Use of exclamation point after interjection.

Correct placement of question mark with quotation marks.

Practice Sentences

1. A owl soared high above the mountain.
2. "Hey" shouted Amy. "Isn't that an eagle"?

Answers

1. An owl soared high above the mountain.
2. "Hey!" shouted Amy. "Isn't that an eagle?"

Day 3

Skills Practiced

Correction of double negative.

Use of period after abbreviation of title.

Use of commas to set off appositive.

Practice Sentences

1. "Don't ever go hiking with no water," warned our guide.
2. Mr Spear a forest ranger told us about the plants along the trail.

Answers

1. "Don't ever go hiking without any water," warned our guide.
2. Mr. Spear, a forest ranger, told us about the plants along the trail.

Day 4

Skills Practiced

Correction of commonly confused words.

Use of subordinating conjunction to combine sentences.

Use of vivid verb to improve style.

Practice Sentences

1. The guide all ready knew the dangers involved in crossing the mountains. He had prepared for the problems we might face.
2. The dark sky told us that a storm was approaching.

Answers

1. Because the guide already knew the dangers involved in crossing the mountains, he had prepared for the problems we might face.
2. The dark sky alerted us that a storm was approaching.

Day 5

Skills Practiced

Use of comma after introductory participial phrase.

Correct pronoun case in compound construction.

Use of adverb to modify a verb.

Practice Sentences

1. Crossing the river everyone walked except the guide and I.
2. The lead horses moved too quick to stay with the oxen.

Answers

1. Crossing the river, everyone walked except the guide and me.
2. The lead horses moved too quickly to stay with the oxen.

Daily Language Practice • Week 3

Day 1

Skills Practiced

Verb agreement with compound subject.

Elimination of unnecessary comma before a conjunction in a compound construction.

Practice Sentences

1. In the book <u>The Accident</u>, Christopher and his dog Bodger is best friends.
2. His mom and dad like to walk, and to canoe.

Answers

1. In the book <u>The Accident</u>, Christopher and his dog Bodger are best friends.
2. His mom and dad like to walk and to canoe.

Day 2

Skills Practiced

Spelling out time written without A.M. or P.M.

Elimination of unnecessary comma before adverb clause.

Elimination of unnecessary comma with a direct quotation.

Practice Sentences

1. It was 8:00 o'clock, when Christopher started walking to the lake.
2. "Bodger!", screamed Christopher.

Answers

1. It was eight o'clock when Christopher started walking to the lake.
2. "Bodger!" screamed Christopher.

Day 3

Skills Practiced

Correction of run-on sentence.

Use of comma after introductory word.

Use of period after abbreviation of title.

Practice Sentences

1. Bodger raced into the road, he was hit by a car.
2. Instantly Christopher knew that even Dr Patel could not help.

Answers

1. Bodger raced into the road, and he was hit by a car.
2. Instantly, Christopher knew that even Dr. Patel could not help.

Day 4

Skills Practiced

Possessive form for plural noun ending in *s*.

Correction of misplaced phrase.

Avoiding *here* and *there* after a demonstrative adjective.

Practice Sentences

1. As the car approached, Christopher saw his parents shocked faces through the window looking at him.
2. "That there truck ran over Bodger," cried Christopher.

Answers

1. As the car approached, Christopher saw his parents' shocked faces looking at him through the window.
2. "That truck ran over Bodger," cried Christopher.

Day 5

Skills Practiced

Use of comma after introductory adverb clause.

Correct form of reflexive pronoun.

Correct use of apostrophe to show possession.

Practice Sentences

1. When dogs are permitted to run free they sometimes find theirselves facing dangerous situations.
2. Christophers' nickname was Crisso.

Answers

1. When dogs are permitted to run free, they sometimes find themselves facing dangerous situations.
2. Christopher's nickname was Crisso.

Daily Language Practice • Week 4

Day 1

Skills Practiced

Use of quotation marks with title of a short story.

Use of 's to show singular possession.

Use of apostrophe in contractions.

Correct use of conjunction *because*.

Practice Sentences

1. In the short story Eleven, it is Rachels eleventh birthday.

2. The reason Rachel doesnt feel eleven is because she hasnt been eleven very long.

Answers

1. In the short story "Eleven," it is Rachel's eleventh birthday.

2. Rachel doesn't feel eleven because she hasn't been eleven very long.

Day 2

Skills Practiced

Use of commas to set off appositive.

Inclusion of closing quotation marks.

Use of a comma and coordinating conjunction to correct run-on sentence.

Use of predicate adjective after linking verb.

Practice Sentences

1. Sylvia Saldivar a girl in Rachel's class said, "The sweater belongs to Rachel.

2. Phyllis Loper finally remembers the sweater is hers Rachel still feels badly.

Answers

1. Sylvia Saldivar, a girl in Rachel's class, said, "The sweater belongs to Rachel."

2. Phyllis Loper finally remembers the sweater is hers, but Rachel still feels bad.

Day 3

Skills Practiced

Formation of irregular verb tense.

Correct capitalization.

Use of end punctuation: question mark.

Practice Sentences

1. In "Aaron's Gift," Aaron knowed how much his gift would mean to his Grandmother.

2. Did Aaron's mom want Aaron to play with Carl.

Answers

1. In "Aaron's Gift," Aaron knew how much his gift would mean to his grandmother.

2. Did Aaron's mom want him to play with Carl?

Day 4

Skills Practiced

Use of colon before a list.

Elimination of *at* following *where*.

Practice Sentences

1. To fix the pigeon's wing, Aaron needed these items popsicle sticks, rags, and tape.
2. Where did Aaron meet Carl and his friends at?

Answers

1. To fix the pigeon's wing, Aaron needed these items: popsicle sticks, rags, and tape.
2. Where did Aaron meet Carl and his friends?

Day 5

Skills Practiced

Use of end punctuation: question mark.

Capitalization of name of month.

Use of comma after the day in a date.

Use of separate sentences to correct run-on sentence.

Practice Sentences

1. What gift do you think Aaron will give his grandmother for her birthday.
2. My birthday is august 2 1983 when is your birthday?

Answers

1. What gift do you think Aaron will give his grandmother for her birthday?
2. My birthday is August 2, 1983. When is your birthday?

Daily Language Practice • Week 5

Day 1

Skills Practiced

Use of commas in a series.

Consistency in spelling out numbers in a series.

Elimination of quotation marks around indirect quotation.

Use of hyphen in compound noun.

Practice Sentences

1. Three adults 7 children one cat and 17 goldfish live in that large farmhouse down the road.

2. In <u>My Side of the Mountain</u>, Sam said that "he wants to live on the land his great grandfather owns."

Answers

1. Three adults, seven children, one cat, and seventeen goldfish live in that large farmhouse down the road.

2. In <u>My Side of the Mountain</u>, Sam said that he wants to live on the land his great-grandfather owns.

Day 2

Skills Practiced

Correction of misplaced phrase.

Use of end punctuation: question mark.

Use of apostrophe with time phrase that modifies a noun.

Practice Sentences

1. Do you think in the woods Sam will be able to survive.

2. Sam thinks he can trap a deer in two hours time.

Answers

1. Do you think Sam will be able to survive in the woods?

2. Sam thinks he can trap a deer in two hours' time.

Day 3

Skills Practiced

Capitalization of proper adjective.

Correct subordinating conjunction.

Correction of faulty subordination.

Use of adverb to modify adjective.

Practice Sentences

1. Sam purchased flint and steel from a chinese store so he could start fires.

2. Because Sam feels real bad, he hasn't had any vitamin C in a long time.

Answers

1. Sam purchased flint and steel from a Chinese store so that he could start fires.

2. Sam feels really bad because he hasn't had any vitamin C in a long time.

Day 4

Skills Practiced

Formation of irregular verb tense.

Correct case of relative pronoun.

Capitalization of name of month.

Practice Sentences

1. Sam catched a falcon, who he named Frightful.

2. On june 20, Sam wrote in his journal, "Frightful will hop from the stump to my fist. She still can't fly."

Answers

1. Sam caught a falcon, whom he named Frightful.

2. On June 20, Sam wrote in his journal, "Frightful will hop from the stump to my fist. She still can't fly."

Day 5

Skills Practiced

Use of separate sentences to correct run-on sentence.

Correct use of commas with address in a sentence.

Correct use of superlative form of an adjective.

Practice Sentences

1. Jean Craighead George has received many letters over the years you can write to her at 20 Williams Street Chappaqua New York 10514.

2. Of all the books I've read, this is the better one.

Answers

1. Jean Craighead George has received many letters over the years. You can write to her at 20 Williams Street, Chappaqua, New York 10514.

2. Of all the books I've read, this is the best one.

Daily Language Practice • Week 6

Day 1

Skills Practiced

Subject and verb agreement.

Use of commas with nonrestrictive clause.

Correction of commonly confused words.

Practice Sentences

1. Do you know there is many plants that grow in areas with little rainfall?
2. The Prickly Pear cactus which is a dessert plant makes a tasty desert.

Answers

1. Do you know there are many plants that grow in areas with little rainfall?
2. The Prickly Pear cactus, which is a desert plant, makes a tasty dessert.

Day 2

Skills Practiced

Correct demonstrative adjective.

Correct comparison of an adjective.

Capitalization of name of country.

Plural possessive form.

Practice Sentences

1. These mountains, which can be seen in the distance, are the higher mountain range in the united states.
2. The womens Olympic biking team practiced by riding the Appalachian Trail.

Answers

1. Those mountains, which can be seen in the distance, are the highest mountain range in the United States.
2. The women's Olympic biking team practiced by riding the Appalachian Trail.

Day 3

Skills Practiced

Use of hyphen with compound adjective.

Use of underlining or italics with the name of an airplane.

Use of active voice to improve style.

Practice Sentences

1. A world famous pilot was forced to land her plane, the Flying Eagle, on a remote island.
2. "I hope someone hears my distress call," she thought. "If not, a shelter will have to be set up by me."

Answers

1. A world-famous pilot was forced to land her plane, the <u>Flying Eagle</u>, on a remote island.
2. "I hope someone hears my distress call," she thought. "If not, I will have to set up a shelter."

Day 4

Skills Practiced

Capitalization of name of geographic feature.

Spelling out numbers through one hundred.

Combining sentences.

Practice Sentences

1. On the ship heading for the great barrier reef off Australia were 3 divers.

2. The reef extends about 1,200 miles. The reef is home to many kinds of fish.

Answers

1. On the ship heading for the Great Barrier Reef off Australia were three divers.

2. The reef extends about 1,200 miles and is home to many kinds of fish.

Day 5

Skills Practiced

Use of underlining or italics with title of book.

Use of parentheses.

Correct comparison of an adjective.

Practice Sentences

1. Nikki read the book Prairie Plants of Illinois for her report.

2. She reported that Big Bluestem (a native plant is the tallest of the two grasses she researched.

Answers

1. Nikki read the book <u>Prairie Plants of Illinois</u> for her report.

2. She reported that Big Bluestem (a native plant) is the taller of the two grasses she researched.

Day 1

Skills Practiced

Use of underlining or italics with the title of a book.

Use of apostrophe in a contraction.

Correction of double negative.

Practice Sentences

1. The book Woodsong was written by Gary Paulsen.
2. Ive lived in Minnesota all my life, but I never saw no bears.

Answers

1. The book <u>Woodsong</u> was written by Gary Paulsen.
2. I've lived in Minnesota all my life, but I have never seen any bears.

Day 2

Skills Practiced

Use of apostrophe to show possession.

Verb tense compatibility.

Use of adverb to modify a verb.

Practice Sentences

1. When the breeze is just right, the smell of the dogs food attracted the bears.
2. The bears snatch the food quick.

Answers

1. When the breeze is just right, the smell of the dogs' food attracts the bears.
2. The bears snatch the food quickly.

Day 3

Skills Practiced

Use of commas with nonrestrictive clause.

Use of quotation marks to show a speaker's exact words.

Formation of irregular contraction.

Practice Sentences

1. Paulsen shouted when he saw the bear who had become a familiar sight rummaging through the burn area.
2. Scarhead wo'nt attack me, Paulsen heard himself saying.

Answers

1. Paulsen shouted when he saw the bear, who had become a familiar sight, rummaging through the burn area.
2. "Scarhead won't attack me," Paulsen heard himself saying.

Day 4

Skills Practiced

- Correction of commonly misused words.
- Pronoun agreement with antecedent.

Practice Sentences

1. Irregardless of how Gary Paulsen felt about Scarhead, he should have been more careful.
2. The wild animals don't usually bother the Paulsen family, but once Ruth did have a deer jump in front of his car.

Answers

1. Regardless of how Gary Paulsen felt about Scarhead, he should have been more careful.
2. The wild animals don't usually bother the Paulsen family, but once Ruth did have a deer jump in front of her car.

Day 5

Skills Practiced

- Use of subordinating conjunction to combine sentences.
- Formation of irregular verb tense.
- Correct pronoun case.

Practice Sentences

1. Paulsen stood in awe. The bear's swiftness amazed him.
2. Paulsen told Eve and I that one must use common sense when living in the woods.

Answers

1. Paulsen stood in awe because the bear's swiftness amazed him.
2. Paulsen told Eve and me that one must use common sense when living in the woods.

Daily Language Practice • Week 8

Day 1

Skills Practiced

Correction of sentence fragment.

Verb tense compatibility.

Combining sentences.

Practice Sentences

1. Clare had one final burst of energy. As she nears the finish line.
2. Clare's teammates stood and cheered wildly. The crowd stood and cheered wildly.

Answers

1. Clare had one final burst of energy as she neared the finish line.
2. Clare's teammates and the crowd stood and cheered wildly.

Day 2

Skills Practiced

Correct past participle of irregular verbs.

Use of apostrophe to show possession.

Elimination of redundancy.

Practice Sentences

1. The piano teacher had took notice of Chris musical skill.
2. In my opinion, I think it was clear that Chris had stole the show.

Answers

1. The piano teacher had taken notice of Chris's musical skill.
2. In my opinion, it was clear that Chris had stolen the show.

Day 3

Skills Practiced

Use of apostrophe in a contraction.

Correction of commonly confused words.

Spelling out numbers under one hundred.

Practice Sentences

1. The exhausted athlete wouldnt accept her coach's advise to rest.
2. Juanita tried desperately to swim the last 5 meters underwater.

Answers

1. The exhausted athlete wouldn't accept her coach's advice to rest.
2. Juanita tried desperately to swim the last five meters underwater.

Day 4

Skills Practiced

Use of comma after introductory participial phrase.

Use of exclamation point after strong interjection.

Correction of double comparison.

Correct past participle of irregular verb.

Practice Sentences

1. Looking up Shawn knew his basketball shot was a hit.
2. "Wow," exclaimed his friend. "That was the most longest three pointer I have ever saw."

Answers

1. Looking up, Shawn knew his basketball shot was a hit.
2. "Wow!" exclaimed his friend. "That was the longest three pointer I have ever seen."

Day 5

Skills Practiced

Use of adverb to modify verb.

Combining sentences.

Correction of commonly confused words.

Subject and verb agreement.

Practice Sentences

1. Gina started the race quick. She soon past her opponents.
2. There's many reasons for Gina's victory.

Answers

1. Gina started the race quickly and soon passed her opponents.
2. There are many reasons for Gina's victory.

Daily Language Practice • Week 9

Day 1

Skills Practiced

Use of quotation marks with title of a short story.

Correction of misplaced modifier.

Capitalization of name of language.

Practice Sentences

1. The Circuit is a short story about migrant workers.
2. Papa only spoke spanish.

Answers

1. "The Circuit" is a short story about migrant workers.
2. Papa spoke only Spanish.

Day 2

Skills Practiced

Correction of a pronoun shift.

Use of apostrophe to show part of date has been omitted.

Capitalization of brand name.

Practice Sentences

1. We hated moving so often, but you accepted it as time went by.
2. Papa drove a 38 black plymouth.

Answers

1. We hated moving so often, but we accepted it as time went by.
2. Papa drove a '38 black Plymouth.

Day 3

Skills Practiced

Correct use of correlative conjunction.

Correct past participle of irregular verb.

Verb agreement with a compound subject joined by *and*.

Practice Sentences

1. Neither Roberto or Panchito had bringed water with them to the fields that day.
2. Roberto and Panchito was in charge of packing the car.

Answers

1. Neither Roberto nor Panchito had brought water with them to the fields that day.
2. Roberto and Panchito were in charge of packing the car.

Day 4

Skills Practiced

Use of apostrophe to show joint possession.

Use of colon with numerals telling time.

Use of periods with abbreviation for time of day.

Correction of commonly confused words.

Practice Sentences

1. Mama's and Papa's bed was the only mattress we owned.

2. The school bus arrived at 715 AM; the blaring of the horn announced it's arrival.

Answers

1. Mama and Papa's bed was the only mattress we owned.

2. The school bus arrived at 7:15 A.M.; the blaring of the horn announced its arrival.

Day 5

Skills Practiced

Use of comma with coordinate adjectives.

Use of hyphen with compound adjectives.

Verb tense compatibility.

Practice Sentences

1. It was a warm cloudy day when Panchito met his sixth grade teacher.

2. Panchito likes listening to the trumpet because it made him feel good.

Answers

1. It was a warm, cloudy day when Panchito met his sixth-grade teacher.

2. Panchito likes listening to the trumpet because it makes him feel good.

Day 1

Skills Practiced

Correct use of parentheses.

Correct past participle of irregular verb.

Use of end punctuation: question mark.

Practice Sentences

1. Laurence Yep 1948– has wrote many books for young people.

2. Did you know that Mr. Yep sold his first book at age eighteen.

Answers

1. Laurence Yep (1948–   ) has written many books for young people.

2. Did you know that Mr. Yep sold his first book at age eighteen?

Day 2

Skills Practiced

Subject and verb agreement.

Capitalization of important words in title.

Elimination of unnecessary comma between subject and verb.

Practice Sentences

1. One of Mr. Yep's books are titled Dragon of the lost sea.

2. Writing stories about his heritage, is important to Mr. Yep.

Answers

1. One of Mr. Yep's books is titled Dragon of the Lost Sea.

2. Writing stories about his heritage is important to Mr. Yep.

Day 3

Skills Practiced

Correction of sentence fragment.

Correct capitalization of name of school subject.

Use of commas in a series.

Practice Sentences

1. After he was challenged by an english teacher. Mr. Yep began his writing career.

2. Setting plot character and theme contribute to the successful development of a story.

Answers

1. After he was challenged by an English teacher, Mr. Yep began his writing career.

2. Setting, plot, character, and theme contribute to the successful development of a story.

Day 4

Skills Practiced

Combining sentences.

Use of apostrophe with amount of money that modifies a noun.

Correct capitalization of name of a season.

Practice Sentences

1. Mr. Yep writes science-fiction stories for young people. Mr. Yep writes fantasy stories for young people.
2. Kate bought twenty dollars worth of science-fiction books during Summer vacation.

Answers

1. Mr. Yep writes science-fiction and fantasy stories for young people.
2. Kate bought twenty dollars' worth of science-fiction books during summer vacation.

Day 5

Skills Practiced

Correct capitalization in name of school course.

Use of hyphen with compound number.

Correct pronoun case.

Practice Sentences

1. We had to write a science-fiction story in our Reading class.
2. Savan wrote twenty eight pages more than me.

Answers

1. We had to write a science-fiction story in our reading class.
2. Savan wrote twenty eight pages more than I.

Daily Language Practice • Week 11

Day 1

Skills Practiced

Correct spelling: *ie/ei*.

Correct use of colon before a list.

Practice Sentences

1. In the story "The Stone," Maibon recieved the gift of his choice from a dwarf named Doli.
2. Doli hoped Maibon would choose one of the following jewels, fine clothes, a hazlewood twig, or an ever-sharp ax.

Answers

1. In the story "The Stone," Maibon received the gift of his choice from a dwarf named Doli.
2. Doli hoped Maibon would choose one of the following: jewels, fine clothes, a hazlewood twig, or an ever-sharp ax.

Day 2

Skills Practiced

Elimination of *here* after demonstrative adjective.

Use of comma to set off a direct quotation.

Use of apostrophe to show omitted letter.

Practice Sentences

1. "This here magic stone looks good to me" thought Maibon to himself.
2. Maibon's wife, Modrona, said "I'm fixin to throw that worthless stone away."

Answers

1. "This magic stone looks good to me," thought Maibon to himself.
2. Maibon's wife, Modrona, said, "I'm fixin' to throw that worthless stone away."

Day 3

Skills Practiced

Use of commas with interrupter.

Pronoun agreement with antecedent.

Formation of irregular verb tense.

Practice Sentences

1. The magic stone believe it or not worked his power.
2. In the morning Maibon was surprised to find that his beard had not grew.

Answers

1. The magic stone, believe it or not, worked its power.
2. In the morning Maibon was surprised to find that his beard had not grown.

Day 4

Skills Practiced

Use of hyphen with the prefix *self-*.

Use of comma after an introductory word.

Correct capitalization of name of a direction.

Practice Sentences

1. The magic stone gave Maibon a feeling of self importance.
2. Immediately Maibon raced West to bury the stone in the wheat field.

Answers

1. The magic stone gave Maibon a feeling of self-importance.
2. Immediately, Maibon raced west to bury the stone in the wheat field.

Day 5

Skills Practiced

Use of comma and coordinating conjunction to combine sentences.

Use of comma after introductory prepositional phrases.

Practice Sentences

1. Maibon didn't want to keep the stone. He threw it away.
2. On a rock near the field the dwarf, Doli, sat waiting for Maibon.

Answers

1. Maibon didn't want to keep the stone, so he threw it away.
2. On a rock near the field, the dwarf, Doli, sat waiting for Maibon.

Daily Language Practice • Week 12

Day 1

Skills Practiced

Correction of sentence fragment.

Capitalization of adjective formed from name of geographic area.

Use of comma after introductory prepositional phrase.

Verb tense compatibility.

Practice Sentences

1. Dragons mythical creatures who are often shown with wings.
2. In the western world dragons symbolized evil and are killed by knights.

Answers

1. Dragons are mythical creatures who are often shown with wings.
2. In the Western world, dragons symbolized evil and were killed by knights.

Day 2

Skills Practiced

Use of quotation marks with title of a short story.

Correction of faulty subordination.

Practice Sentences

1. In the fairy tale The Dragon and the Monkey, the dragon's wife wants a monkey's heart.
2. The monkey realizes he is in danger, after he thinks fast and outsmarts the dragon.

Answers

1. In the fairy tale "The Dragon and the Monkey," the dragon's wife wants a monkey's heart.
2. After the monkey realizes he is in danger, he thinks fast and outsmarts the dragon.

Day 3

Skills Practiced

Correct subordinating conjunction *as*.

Correction of commonly confused words.

Use of hyphen with compound number.

Practice Sentences

1. The dragon roamed the countryside and destroyed it like we had predicted.
2. The dragon, who's wingspan extended over twenty five feet, terrorized the villagers.

Answers

1. The dragon roamed the countryside and destroyed it as we had predicted.
2. The dragon, whose wingspan extended over twenty-five feet, terrorized the villagers.

Day 4

Skills Practiced

Correct use of apostrophe to show plural possession.

Use of subordinating conjunction to combine sentences.

Use of comma after introductory word.

Practice Sentences

1. Ten knight's horses all reared in fright. The dragon's shadow blanketed them.

2. Personally I would not want to encounter a dragon.

Answers

1. Ten knights' horses all reared in fright when the dragon's shadow blanketed them.

2. Personally, I would not want to encounter a dragon.

Day 5

Skills Practiced

Correct past participle of irregular verb.

Use of exclamation point to show strong emotion.

Correction of misplaced modifier.

Practice Sentences

1. The dragon must be drove from the countryside now.

2. Frightening the villagers, the kind knight met the dragon.

Answers

1. The dragon must be driven from the countryside now!

2. Frightening the villagers, the dragon met the kind knight.

Day 1

Skills Practiced

Use of correct form of reflexive pronoun.

Capitalization of name of specific place.

Correction of commonly confused words.

Practice Sentences

1. In the short story "The All-American Slurp," the Lin family embarrassed theirselves the first time they ate celery.

2. The Lin family had arrived recently from china and had trouble learning they're table manners.

Answers

1. In the short story "The All-American Slurp," the Lin family embarrassed themselves the first time they ate celery.

2. The Lin family had arrived recently from China and had trouble learning their table manners.

Day 2

Skills Practiced

Spelling out large numbers expressed in one or two words.

Correct use of apostrophe to show possession.

Subject and verb agreement.

Practice Sentences

1. One of the items the Lin family purchased was a 1000-piece jigsaw puzzle.

2. Many dresses in the narrators closet fits Meg.

Answers

1. One of the items the Lin family purchased was a one-thousand-piece jigsaw puzzle.

2. Many dresses in the narrator's closet fit Meg.

Day 3

Skills Practiced

Use of underlining or italics with foreign words.

Correction of unclear pronoun reference.

Practice Sentences

1. When the Lin family went to dinner, Mr. Lin noticed that one of the specialties was paté en croute.

2. Since Mrs. Lin had studied books on American culture, she knew they should tip their soup bowls to eat the soup.

Answers

1. When the Lin family went to dinner, Mr. Lin noticed that one of the specialties was <u>paté en croute</u>.

2. Since Mrs. Lin had studied books on American culture, she knew the family should tip their soup bowls to eat the soup.

Day 4

Skills Practiced

Capitalization of a person's name.

Elimination of unnecessary colon before a list.

Avoiding *here* and *there* after a demonstrative adjective.

Use of adverb to modify an adjective.

Practice Sentences

1. When our neighbors came for dinner, mom served: fruit, vegetables, rolls, and sliced turkey.
2. "This here fruit salad looks real good," said Ms. Gowe.

Answers

1. When our neighbors came for dinner, Mom served fruit, vegetables, rolls, and sliced turkey.
2. "This fruit salad looks really good," said Ms. Gowe.

Day 5

Skills Practiced

Use of comma after introductory participle.

Correct spelling of plural noun.

Elimination of commas with a restrictive clause.

Practice Sentences

1. Smiling Annalise garnishes her salad with many dried tomatos.
2. Do you think the restaurant, where the Lin family ate, became one of their favorites?

Answers

1. Smiling, Annalise garnishes her salad with many dried tomatoes.
2. Do you think the restaurant where the Lin family ate became one of their favorites?

Day 1

Skills Practiced

Use of *different from.*

Correct relative pronoun.

Use of commas with interrupter.

Practice Sentences

1. Foods and eating customs play an important role in helping to promote awareness of a culture different than your own.

2. Some foods who have ethnic names have no connection with their ethnic name; French toast for example is not served in France.

Answers

1. Foods and eating customs play an important role in helping to promote awareness of a culture different from your own.

2. Some foods that have ethnic names have no connection with their ethnic name; French toast, for example, is not served in France.

Day 2

Skills Practiced

Use of comma with coordinate adjectives.

Pronoun agreement with antecedent.

Practice Sentences

1. Strong hot spices are used frequently to prepare Korean foods.

2. Kyle had hated spicy food at first, but he learned to like them over time.

Answers

1. Strong, hot spices are used frequently to prepare Korean foods.

2. Kyle had hated spicy food at first, but he learned to like it over time.

Day 3

Skills Practiced

Capitalization of name of geographic area.

Correction of sentence fragment.

Correction of faulty subordination.

Practice Sentences

1. A food popular in the south is hominy grits. Served for breakfast or as a side dish with meat.

2. Because the Japanese diet is low in fat, the Japanese eat eight times more fish than Americans eat.

Answers

1. A food popular in the South is hominy grits, which is served for breakfast or as a side dish with meat.

2. The Japanese diet is low in fat because the Japanese eat eight times more fish than Americans eat.

Day 4

Skills Practiced

Use of comma after introductory prepositional phrase.

Use of active voice to improve style.

Elimination of redundancy.

Practice Sentences

1. In San Francisco in the 1800's the fortune cookie was made for the public to enjoy by a Chinese American man.

2. The reason I like Mexican food is because I like spices.

Answers

1. In San Francisco in the 1800's, a Chinese American man made the fortune cookie for the public to enjoy.

2. I like Mexican food because I like spices.

Day 5

Skills Practiced

Use of comma after introductory subordinate clause.

Pronoun agreement with antecedent.

Correct use of colon before a list.

Use of semicolons in a series containing commas.

Practice Sentences

1. In China if you want to wish a friend good luck you present them with an orange.

2. Koreans enjoy a wide variety of foods including the following edible greens such as watercress, water lily roots, and dandelions, egg rolls, soups such as bean sprout.

Answers

1. In China if you want to wish a friend good luck, you present him or her with an orange.

2. Koreans enjoy a wide variety of foods including the following: edible greens such as watercress, water lily roots, dandelions; egg rolls; soups such as bean sprout.

Daily Language Practice • Week 15

Day 1

Skills Practiced

Capitalization of important words in title.

Use of underlining or italics with title of book.

Use of comma with interrupter.

Practice Sentences

1. "The sound of summer running" is from a book by Ray Bradbury called Dandelion Wine.
2. By the way Douglas wants a pair of new tennis shoes in the story.

Answers

1. "The Sound of Summer Running" is from a book by Ray Bradbury called <u>Dandelion Wine</u>.
2. By the way, Douglas wants a pair of new tennis shoes in the story.

Day 2

Skills Practiced

Use of semicolon between main clauses.

Verb tense compatibility.

Spelling out times expressed without the abbreviations A.M. or P.M.

Practice Sentences

1. Douglas has to do more than just want new shoes he has to work for his new shoes.
2. Douglas was at the store when it opens its doors at 9:00.

Answers

1. Douglas has to do more than just want new shoes; he has to work for his new shoes.
2. Douglas was at the store when it opened its doors at nine o'clock.

Day 3

Skills Practiced

Capitalization of spelled-out numeral for a special day of the month.

Correct placement of question mark with quotation marks.

Pronoun agreement with antecedent.

Practice Sentences

1. Jill asked, "Do you have any special plans for the fourth of July"?
2. Each of Jill's girlfriends shared their holiday plans.

Answers

1. Jill asked, "Do you have any special plans for the Fourth of July?"
2. Each of Jill's girlfriends shared her holiday plans.

Day 4

Skills Practiced

Correction of double negative.

Elimination of quotation marks around indirect quotation.

Practice Sentences

1. The discussion led Jill to complain bitterly that she didn't plan to do nothing over summer vacation.

2. Needless to say, Jill was thrilled when Marta said that "her family was going to the beach and asked Jill to go with them."

Answers

1. The discussion led Jill to complain bitterly that she didn't plan to do anything over summer vacation.

2. Needless to say, Jill was thrilled when Marta said that her family was going to the beach and asked Jill to go with them.

Day 5

Skills Practiced

Use of colon after greeting of a business letter.

Inclusion of opening quotation marks.

Use of separate sentences to correct run-on sentence.

Correct subordinating conjunction *as if*.

Practice Sentences

1. Isenia began her business letter to the shoe manufacturer as follows:

    Dear Sir or Madam,

2. Isenia wrote, I am very happy with my new shoes they make me feel like I can fly!"

Answers

1. Isenia began her business letter to the shoe manufacturer as follows:

    Dear Sir or Madam:

2. Isenia wrote, "I am very happy with my new shoes. They make me feel as if I can fly!"

Daily Language Practice • Week 16

Day 1

Skills Practiced

Elimination of *at* after *where*.

Capitalization of name of nationality.

Correct end punctuation: period.

Use of correlative conjunction.

Practice Sentences

1. In the book <u>The Phantom Tollbooth</u>, Milo wonders where the lethargarians live at?

2. Not only does Milo visit some very strange places, he meets some very unusual characters.

Answers

1. In the book <u>The Phantom Tollbooth</u>, Milo wonders where the Lethargarians live.

2. Not only does Milo visit some very strange places, but also he meets some very unusual characters.

Day 2

Skills Practiced

Use of hyphen with compound adjective.

Use of apostrophe to show plural of word as word.

Use of period to separate dollars from cents.

Practice Sentences

1. A merchant was selling reasonably-priced bags of "happys" at the Word Market in Dictionopolis.

2. Do you think you could buy a bag of used words there for as little as $3 50¢?

Answers

1. A merchant was selling reasonably priced bags of "happy's" at the Word Market in Dictionopolis.

2. Do you think you could buy a bag of used words there for as little as $3.50?

Day 3

Skills Practiced

Use of apostrophe to show plural of letter.

Use of colon with numerals telling time.

Use of ellipsis points to signal an incomplete thought.

Practice Sentences

1. When Milo visited Dictionopolis, he noticed all the doors were shaped like <u>H</u>s and <u>A</u>s.

2. Lethargarian 3 started to explain, "From 930 A.M. to 1130 A.M. we take our"

Answers

1. When Milo visited Dictionopolis, he noticed all the doors were shaped like <u>H</u>'s and <u>A</u>'s.

2. Lethargarian 3 started to explain, "From 9:30 A.M. to 11:30 A.M. we take our…"

	Skills Practiced	**Practice Sentences**
Day 4	Use of commas with a split quotation.	1. "Words and numbers" Reason said "Are of equal importance."
	Correct capitalization in a split quotation.	2. In the end it was Rhyme's and Reason's good sense that caused them to be banished to the Castle-in-the-Air.
	Correct indication of joint possession.	**Answers**
		1. "Words and numbers," Reason said, "are of equal importance."
		2. In the end it was Rhyme and Reason's good sense that caused them to be banished to the Castle-in-the-Air.

	Skills Practiced	**Practice Sentences**
Day 5	Capitalization of title before person's name.	1. After reading <u>The Phantom Tollbooth</u>, cousin Ankur and me wanted to shop at the Word Market.
	Correct pronoun case in compound construction.	2. Of all the imaginary places described in <u>The Phantom Tollbooth</u>, the Doldrums is my less favorite place.
	Correct comparison of an adjective.	**Answers**
		1. After reading <u>The Phantom Tollbooth</u>, Cousin Ankur and I wanted to shop at the Word Market.
		2. Of all the imaginary places described in <u>The Phantom Tollbooth</u>, the Doldrums is my least favorite place.

Daily Language Practice • Week 17

Day 1

Skills Practiced

Use of separate sentences to correct run-on sentence.

Use of conjunctive adverb to clarify cause-and-effect relationship.

Correction of commonly confused words.

Practice Sentences

1. The ideas of space travel and manned space stations are not new, people have fantasized and written about them since the 1860's.
2. The spaceship could not dock at the space station; it returned to Earth without emptying it's cargo.

Answers

1. The ideas of space travel and manned space stations are not new. People have fantasized and written about them since the 1860's.
2. The spaceship could not dock at the space station; as a result, it returned to Earth without emptying its cargo.

Day 2

Skills Practiced

Use of comma after introductory prepositional phrases.

Correct verb tense.

Correction of government agency abbreviation.

Correct use of parentheses.

Practice Sentences

1. Since the early days of space travel meteorites concerned scientists.
2. Nasa National Aeronautics and Space Administration is coordinating an international effort to build a space station.

Answers

1. Since the early days of space travel, meteorites have concerned scientists.
2. NASA (National Aeronautics and Space Administration) is coordinating an international effort to build a space station.

Day 3

Skills Practiced

Elimination of unnecessary hyphen with compound modifier.

Elimination of capitalization with common noun.

Use of commas to separate parts of an address.

Practice Sentences

1. The room sizes of the space station were well-defined in the architects' floor plan.
2. Meg's Cousin received information about space travel by writing to NASA at 2100 Brookpark Road Cleveland Ohio 44135.

Answers

1. The room sizes of the space station were well defined in the architects' floor plan.
2. Meg's cousin received information about space travel by writing to NASA at 2100 Brookpark Road, Cleveland, Ohio 44135.

Day 4

Skills Practiced

Use of underlining or italics with words used as words.

Subject and verb agreement.

Use of comma after day and year in a date.

Use of underlining or italics with the name of a spacecraft.

Practice Sentences

1. Space explorers, who are called astronauts in the United States and cosmonauts in Russia, undergo extensive training, both physical and intellectual.

2. There is many milestones in space travel, including the historic launching on October 4 1957 of the first human-made satellite Sputnik I.

Answers

1. Space explorers, who are called <u>astronauts</u> in the United States and <u>cosmonauts</u> in Russia, undergo extensive training, both physical and intellectual.

2. There are many milestones in space travel, including the historic launching on October 4, 1957, of the first human-made satellite <u>Sputnik I</u>.

Day 5

Skills Practiced

Use of comma after introductory participial phrase.

Verb tense compatibility.

Use of capitalization in an outline.

Practice Sentences

1. For her report on space travel Rosa researched her topic and outlines her ideas.

2. 1. important events in space travel
   a. space flights with humans
   b. space flights without humans

Answers

1. For her report on space travel, Rosa researched her topic and outlined her ideas.

2. I. Important events in space travel
   A. Space flights with humans
   B. Space flights without humans

Daily Language Practice • Week 18

Day 1

Skills Practiced

Use of relative clause to combine sentences.

Elimination of unnecessary comma.

Practice Sentences

1. The book <u>A Wrinkle in Time</u> was written by Madeleine L'Engle. <u>A Wrinkle in Time</u> won the Newbery Medal in 1963.
2. In the story Meg's father is a scientist who disappears, while working on a secret project.

Answers

1. The book <u>A Wrinkle in Time</u>, which won the Newbery Medal in 1963, was written by Madeleine L'Engle.
2. In the story Meg's father is a scientist who disappears while working on a secret project.

Day 2

Skills Practiced

Use of commas in a series.

Avoiding *here* and *there* after a demonstrative adjective.

Pronoun agreement with antecedent.

Practice Sentences

1. Meg meets three unearthly creatures named Mrs. Whatsit Mrs. Who and Mrs. Which.
2. "Meg, that there black shadow is the evil you must overcome to get her father back," explained Mrs. Whatsit.

Answers

1. Meg meets three unearthly creatures named Mrs. Whatsit, Mrs. Who, and Mrs. Which.
2. "Meg, that black shadow is the evil you must overcome to get your father back," explained Mrs. Whatsit.

Day 3

Skills Practiced

Capitalization of first word of quotation.

Use of exclamation point to show strong emotion.

Elimination of comma before coordinating conjunction in a compound predicate.

Practice Sentences

1. Just as they were about to tesseract, Meg screamed, "wait."
2. In the story, tesseracting is a way of traveling through space, and is considered the fifth dimension.

Answers

1. Just as they were about to tesseract, Meg screamed, "Wait!"
2. In the story, tesseracting is a way of traveling through space and is considered the fifth dimension.

Day 4

Skills Practiced

Capitalization of first word of a sentence.

Correction of sentence fragment.

Elimination of question mark with indirect question.

Practice Sentences

1. one of Meg's nicknames was Megaparsec. Which had been given to her by her father.
2. Ted asked if the new student had a nickname?

Answers

1. One of Meg's nicknames was Megaparsec, which had been given to her by her father.
2. Ted asked if the new student had a nickname.

Day 5

Skills Practiced

Correct pronoun case.

Use of apostrophe to show possession.

Use of quotation marks with the title of a short work.

Practice Sentences

1. Juanita likes science fiction stories more than me.
2. Franks report Beyond the Milky Way was a mixture of fact and fantasy.

Answers

1. Juanita likes science fiction stories more than I.
2. Frank's report "Beyond the Milky Way" was a mixture of fact and fantasy.

Daily Language Practice • Week 19

Day 1

Skills Practiced

Elimination of unnecessary colon before a list.

Correct placement of question mark with quotation marks.

Correct end punctuation.

Practice Sentences

1. There are many resources available in the public library including: atlases, newspapers, dictionaries, thesauruses, and magazines.

2. "Before I continue, are there any other questions about your report" the teacher asked?

Answers

1. There are many resources available in the public library including atlases, newspapers, dictionaries, thesauruses, and magazines.

2. "Before I continue, are there any other questions about your report?" the teacher asked.

Day 2

Skills Practiced

Correction of faulty subordination.

Use of correlative conjunction.

Verb tense compatibility.

Practice Sentences

1. Because Kim went to the library, she had to research her report on women in science.

2. Not only did Kim use the card catalog to look up information, she uses the computer.

Answers

1. Kim went to the library because she had to research her report on women in science.

2. Not only did Kim use the card catalog to look up information, but also she used the computer.

Day 3

Skills Practiced

Correction of misplaced modifier.

Correct formation of plural noun.

Subject and verb agreement.

Practice Sentences

1. Filled with maps of the newly formed countrys, Evan referred to the atlas as he researched his report on the changing face of Europe.

2. Each of the resource books on the bookshelves have a copyright date in the 1990's.

Answers

1. Evan referred to the atlas filled with maps of the newly formed countries as he researched his report on the changing face of Europe.

2. Each of the resource books on the bookshelves has a copyright date in the 1990's.

Day 4

Skills Practiced

Correct formation of plural noun.

Capitalization of religious term.

Subject and verb agreement.

Practice Sentences

1. A recent article in the local paper discussed the Jewish celebration's of rosh hashanah and yom kippur.

2. Many a magazine article and book have been written on the topic of endangered animals.

Answers

1. A recent article in the local paper discussed the Jewish celebrations of Rosh Hashanah and Yom Kippur.

2. Many a magazine article and book has been written on the topic of endangered animals.

Day 5

Skills Practiced

Correct pronoun case in compound construction.

Elimination of capitalization with common noun.

Use of comma after introductory elements.

Revision of sentence ending with a preposition.

Practice Sentences

1. After school Neil and me agreed to meet at the University library.

2. In the last few minutes before the library closed Marci located the magazine she had been looking for.

Answers

1. After school Neil and I agreed to meet at the university library.

2. In the last few minutes before the library closed, Marci located the magazine she had been trying to find.

Daily Language Practice • Week 20

Day 1

Skills Practiced

Use of quotation marks with title of a short work.

Correction of double comparison.

Practice Sentences

1. My Papa, Mark Twain is a biographical sketch of Samuel Clemens written by Susy Clemens, his daughter.
2. Susy Clemens believed her father was the most loveliest man she had ever seen.

Answers

1. "My Papa, Mark Twain" is a biographical sketch of Samuel Clemens written by Susy Clemens, his daughter.
2. Susy Clemens believed her father was the loveliest man she had ever seen.

Day 2

Skills Practiced

Use of comma before coordinating conjunction in a compound sentence.

Correct past participle of irregular verb.

Use of separate sentences to correct run-on sentence.

Practice Sentences

1. Susy's journal entry had many grammar and spelling mistakes but it gave her father a feeling of great pride.
2. One passage reads, "The names that he has give our different cats are really remarkably funny, they are named Stray Kit, Abner, Motley, . . . "

Answers

1. Susy's journal entry had many grammar and spelling mistakes, but it gave her father a feeling of great pride.
2. One passage reads, "The names that he has given our different cats are really remarkably funny. They are named Stray Kit, Abner, Motley, . . . "

Day 3

Skills Practiced

Use of comma with coordinate adjectives.

Correction of sentence fragment.

Spelling out numbers through one hundred.

Correction of misplaced modifier.

Practice Sentences

1. Susy saw her father as a warm humorous individual. Misunderstood by many.
2. Susy, who was 13 years old only when she wrote "My Papa, Mark Twain," died at the age of twenty-four.

Answers

1. Susy saw her father as a warm, humorous individual. He was misunderstood by many.
2. Susy, who was only thirteen years old when she wrote "My Papa, Mark Twain," died at the age of twenty-four.

Day 4	**Skills Practiced**	**Practice Sentences**
	Capitalization of important words in title of literary work.	1. Anne Frank's <u>The diary of a young girl</u> is a journal of her experiences as a Jewish girl in Holland during World War II.
	Correction of hyphen used with compound modifier.	2. The recently-published book <u>Zlata's Diary</u> is a young girl's journal about Sarajevo her thoughts and feelings about her life as she is surrounded by war.
	Use of dash to emphasize additional information.	**Answers**
		1. Anne Frank's <u>The Diary of a Young Girl</u> is a journal of her experiences as a Jewish girl in Holland during World War II.
		2. The recently published book <u>Zlata's Diary</u> is a young girl's journal about Sarajevo—her thoughts and feelings about her life as she is surrounded by war.

Day 5	**Skills Practiced**	**Practice Sentences**
	Use of apostrophe in a contraction.	1. Helena doesnt write in her journal as often as me.
	Correct pronoun case.	2. Greg's journal entry began, "I will always remember Monday, October 3 1994 as the day of the big surprise . . . "
	Use of comma after day and year in a date.	**Answers**
		1. Helena doesn't write in her journal as often as I.
		2. Greg's journal entry began, "I will always remember Monday, October 3, 1994, as the day of the big surprise . . . "

Daily Language Practice • Week 21

Day 1

Skills Practiced

Revision of wordy sentence.

Use of adverb to modify a verb.

Correction of unclear pronoun reference.

Practice Sentences

1. Biographies can contain errors in spite of the fact that they are researched good.
2. Russell Freedman researched information about Abraham Lincoln before writing about his life.

Answers

1. Biographies can contain errors even though they are researched well.
2. Russell Freedman researched information about Abraham Lincoln before writing about Lincoln's life.

Day 2

Skills Practiced

Capitalization of title used in direct address.

Correct pronoun case.

Practice Sentences

1. After he won a seat in the New York State Senate in 1910, Franklin Roosevelt often heard people ask, "senator, do you wish to comment on this point?"
2. Him and his wife, Eleanor, worked very hard on public isuues.

Answers

1. After he won a seat in the New York State Senate in 1910, Franklin Roosevelt often heard people ask, "Senator, do you wish to comment on this point?"
2. He and his wife, Eleanor, worked very hard on public issues.

Day 3

Skills Practiced

Use of predicate adjective after linking verb.

Correction of sentence fragment.

Use of comma after introductory participial phrase.

Use of hyphen with the prefix self-.

Practice Sentences

1. At first Eleanor Roosevelt appeared timidly. But emerged a strong, purposeful woman.
2. Studying abroad Eleanor gained self confidence.

Answers

1. At first Eleanor Roosevelt appeared timid, but she emerged a strong, purposeful woman.
2. Studying abroad, Eleanor gained self-confidence.

Day 4

Skills Practiced

Use of active voice to improve style.

Revision of stringy sentence.

Practice Sentences

1. Many books were written by Theodor Geisel, who is better known as Dr. Seuss.

2. Theodor Geisel also wrote films and some of these films won awards and one film won an Academy Award in 1946.

Answers

1. Theodor Geisel, who is better known as Dr. Seuss, wrote many books.

2. Theodor Geisel also wrote films. Some of these films won awards; in fact, one film won an Academy Award in 1946.

Day 5

Skills Practiced

Subject and verb agreement.

Correct use of definite article.

Use of parentheses.

Use of active voice to improve style.

Practice Sentences

1. Marie Curie, together with her husband, Pierre, were awarded a Nobel Prize for Physics in 1903.

2. Two Nobel Prizes, one for Physics 1903 and one for Chemistry 1911, were received by Marie Curie.

Answers

1. Marie Curie, together with her husband, Pierre, was awarded the Nobel Prize for Physics in 1903.

2. Marie Curie received two Nobel Prizes, one for Physics (1903) and one for Chemistry (1911).

Daily Language Practice • Week 22

Day 1

Skills Practiced

Correct use of conjunction *because*.

Correction use of correlative conjunction.

Practice Sentences

1. The reason Chief Seattle wrote his "Letter to the U.S. Government" is because he wanted to persuade his readers to respect the land.
2. Chief Seattle could understand neither the clatter of the cities or the senseless killing of the buffalo.

Answers

1. Chief Seattle wrote his "Letter to the U.S. Government" because he wanted to persuade his readers to respect the land.
2. Chief Seattle could understand neither the clatter of the cities nor the senseless killing of the buffalo.

Day 2

Skills Practiced

Use of apostrophe in a contraction.

Correction of misplaced modifier.

Practice Sentences

1. Ill want to read Chief Seattle's letter again to understand it fully.
2. Chief Seattle influences people with strong messages.

Answers

1. I'll want to read Chief Seattle's letter again to understand it fully.
2. With strong messages, Chief Seattle influences people.

Day 3

Skills Practiced

Correct placement of question mark with quotation marks.

Spelling out name of state in a sentence.

Practice Sentences

1. What do you think Chief Seattle meant when he said, "The end of living and the beginning of survival?"
2. The city of Seattle, WA, is named for Chief Seattle.

Answers

1. What do you think Chief Seattle meant when he said, "The end of living and the beginning of survival"?
2. The city of Seattle, Washington, is named for Chief Seattle.

Day 4

Skills Practiced	Practice Sentences
Use of periods with initials.	1. Another letter writer was CS Lewis, who wrote advice on good and bad english.
Capitalization of name of a language.	2. Your sure to be a good writer, if you follow Mr. Lewis's advice.
Correction of commonly confused words.	**Answers**
Elimination of comma with a restrictive clause.	1. Another letter writer was C. S. Lewis, who wrote advice on good and bad English.
	2. You're sure to be a good writer if you follow Mr. Lewis's advice.

Day 5

Skills Practiced	Practice Sentences
Combining sentences.	1. F. Scott Fitzgerald was a letter writer who wrote a list of things to worry about. He wrote a list of things not to worry about. He wrote a list of things to think about.
Use of subordinating conjunction to combine sentences.	2. F. Scott Fitzgerald had several nicknames for his daughter. F. Scott Fitzgerald did not appreciate her calling him by a nickname.
	Answers
	1. F. Scott Fitzerald was a letter writer who wrote a list of things to worry about, a list of things not to worry about, and a list of things to think about.
	2. Although F. Scott Fitzerald had several nicknames for his daughter, he did not appreciate her calling him by a nickname.

Daily Language Practice • Week 23

Day 1

Skills Practiced

Use of coordinating conjunction to combine sentences.

Revision of sentence ending with a preposition.

Correction of pronoun shift.

Practice Sentences

1. Mitch plans to write a letter. He can't find a pen to write with.
2. Consuela likes writing business letters because you have to be very precise.

Answers

1. Mitch plans to write a letter, but he can't find a pen to use.
2. Consuela likes writing business letters because she has to be very precise.

Day 2

Skills Practiced

Correct past participle of irregular verb.

Subject and verb agreement.

Use of vivid verb to improve style.

Correct pronoun case.

Practice Sentences

1. Some of the letters that Kenji had wrote to his grandmother shows humor.
2. In one letter Kenji said, "Jared and me designed the award-winning party invitation!"

Answers

1. Some of the letters that Kenji had written to his grandmother show humor.
2. In one letter Kenji exclaimed, "Jared and I designed the award-winning party invitation!"

Day 3

Skills Practiced

Combining sentences.

Elimination of empty sentence.

Practice Sentences

1. I like the book <u>Dear Mr. Henshaw</u>. My friends like the book <u>Dear Mr. Henshaw</u>, too.
2. A good book is <u>Dear Dad, Love Laurie</u>, which is about a sixth-grade girl who writes letters to her divorced dad. It is another book to read.

Answers

1. My friends and I like the book <u>Dear Mr. Henshaw</u>.
2. Another good book to read is <u>Dear Dad, Love Laurie</u>, which is about a sixth-grade girl who writes letters to her divorced dad.

Day 4	**Skills Practiced**	**Practice Sentences**
	Correction of faulty parallel structure.	1. Camella's classmates researched, had written, and sent letters about environmental problems to the President.
	Pronoun agreement with antecedent.	2. Each student used the following address on their envelopes:
	Use of comma with an address on an envelope.	The White House
		1600 Pennsylvania Ave.
		Washington D.C. 20500
		Answers
		1. Camella's classmates researched, wrote, and sent letters about environmental problems to the President.
		2. Each student used the following address on his or her envelope:
		The White House
		1600 Pennsylvania Ave.
		Washington, D.C. 20500

Day 5	**Skills Practiced**	**Practice Sentences**
	Capitalization of important words in greeting of letter.	1. Ira began his business letter this way:
		dear Mr. Negrone,
	Use of colon after greeting of a business letter.	2. Ira ended his business letter in the following way:
	Use of comma after closing of business letter.	Respectfully yours
		Answers
		1. Ira began his business letter this way:
		Dear Mr. Negrone:
		2. Ira ended his business letter in the following way:
		Respectfully yours,

Daily Language Practice • Week 24

Day 1

Skills Practiced

Use of semicolon to correct run-on sentence.

Correction of misplaced modifier.

Correction of commonly misspelled word.

Practice Sentences

1. The world is filled with mysteries, we may only solve some of them.

2. Many scientists succede in making new discoveries.

Answers

1. The world is filled with mysteries; we may solve only some of them.

2. Many scientists succeed in making new discoveries.

Day 2

Skills Practiced

Use of commas with interrupter.

Correct spelling of plural noun.

Combining sentences.

Practice Sentences

1. Stonehenge for example has intrigued people for centurys.

2. Archeologists have uncovered details about Stonehenge. Astronomers have uncovered details about Stonehenge. Geologists have uncovered details about Stonehenge.

Answers

1. Stonehenge, for example, has intrigued people for centuries.

2. Archeologists, astronomers, and geologists have uncovered details about Stonehenge.

Day 3

Skills Practiced

Pronoun-antecedent agreement.

Subject and verb agreement.

Revision of sentence ending with a preposition.

Practice Sentences

1. Each of the scientists has their ideas about Stonehenge.

2. Not even one of the scientists who investigated Stonehenge are able to answer all the questions this remarkable mystery is about.

Answers

1. Each of the scientists has his or her ideas about Stonehenge.

2. Not even one of the scientists who investigated Stonehenge is able to answer all the questions about this remarkable mystery.

Day 4

Skills Practiced

Use of subordinating conjunction to combine sentences.

Use of hyphen in fraction.

Use of numerals and words for round numbers ending in millions.

Practice Sentences

1. The Grand Canyon in Colorado is not a mystery. The Grand Canyon is a natural wonder.

2. The upper two thirds of the Grand Canyon walls are made of sedimentary rock that was deposited six hundred million to two hundred million years ago.

Answers

1. Although the Grand Canyon in Colorado is not a mystery, it is a natural wonder.

2. The upper two-thirds of the Grand Canyon walls are made of sedimentary rock that was deposited 600 million to 200 million years ago.

Day 5

Skills Practiced

Revision of wordy sentence.

Use of apostrophe to show possession.

Use of commas with a split quotation.

Practice Sentences

1. Many mysteries remain unsolved in spite of the fact that scientists methods for analyzing data are improving.

2. "Do you think" the teacher asked "any of you will become archeologists?"

Answers

1. Many mysteries remain unsolved even though scientists' methods for analyzing data are improving.

2. "Do you think," the teacher asked, "any of you will become archeologists?"

Daily Language Practice • Week 25

Day 1

Skills Practiced

Use of *different from*.

Eliminating *here* and *there* after a demonstrative adjective.

Practice Sentences

1. Writing poetry is different than writing narratives or other forms of literature.
2. That there book of poems by Eric Carle is my favorite.

Answers

1. Writing poetry is different from writing narratives or other forms of literature.
2. That book of poems by Eric Carle is my favorite.

Day 2

Skills Practiced

Use of comma after introductory prepositional phrases.

Correct comparison of an adjective.

Revision of misplaced modifier.

Use of adverb to modify adjective.

Practice Sentences

1. Of all the poems in Shel Silverstein's <u>A Light in the Attic</u> the poem I like more is "Whatif."
2. I relate to "Whatif" because it reflects how I feel at night when I go to bed real well.

Answers

1. Of all the poems in Shel Silverstein's <u>A Light in the Attic</u>, the poem I like most is "Whatif."
2. I relate to "Whatif" because it reflects really well how I feel at night when I go to bed.

Day 3

Skills Practiced

Varying sentence beginning to improve style.

Use of hyphen with compound adjective.

Use of comma to set off a direct quotation.

Correct placement of question mark with quotation marks.

Practice Sentences

1. David McCord expresses his deep felt interest in books in his poem "Books Fall Open."
2. What does Mr. McCord mean when he says "Books fall open, you fall in, . . . ?"

Answers

1. In his poem "Books Fall Open," David McCord expresses his deep-felt interest in books.
2. What does Mr. McCord mean when he says, "Books fall open, you fall in, . . . "?

Day 4

Skills Practiced	Practice Sentences
Use of comma after introductory prepositional phrases. Elimination of double negative. Use of adverb form.	1. In "Winter Poem" by Nikki Giovanni the author doesn't use no punctuation. 2. This lack of punctuation gives the impression of a snowflake falling gentle to earth. **Answers** 1. In "Winter Poem" by Nikki Giovanni, the author doesn't use any punctuation. 2. This lack of punctuation gives the impression of a snowflake falling gently to earth.

Day 5

Skills Practiced	Practice Sentences

Revision of choppy sentences.
Correct use of capitalization in name of school courses.
Use of 's to form singular possessive.
	1. Chris wrote a poem. He wrote it for his creative writing 102 class. He titled the poem "Life."
	2. Here is Chris' poem.
	
	    Life is hard.
	    Life is easy.
	    Life is fun.
	    Life is a puzzle
	    of work and rest.
	
	Answers
	
	1. For his Creative Writing 102 class, Chris wrote a poem titled "Life."
	2. Here is Chris's poem.
	
	    Life is hard.
	    Life is easy.
	    Life is fun.
	    Life is a puzzle
	    of work and rest.

Daily Language Practice • Week 26

Day 1

Skills Practiced

Pronoun agreement with antecedent.

Use of appositive to combine sentences.

Practice Sentences

1. Some poets, such as Lewis Carroll, use humor to present his message.

2. "The Walrus and the Carpenter" is one of Lewis Carroll's famous poems. It is a nonsense poem.

Answers

1. Some poets, such as Lewis Carroll, use humor to present their message.

2. "The Walrus and the Carpenter," a nonsense poem, is one of Lewis Carroll's famous poems.

Day 2

Skills Practiced

Use of subordinating conjunction to combine sentences.

Revision of wordy sentence.

Practice Sentences

1. In the poem "The Walrus and the Carpenter," the oysters wear shoes, which is very odd. They don't have any feet.

2. What I want to say is that it also doesn't make sense that the sun is shining in the middle of the night.

Answers

1. In the poem "The Walrus and the Carpenter," the oysters wear shoes, which is very odd because they don't have any feet.

2. It also doesn't make sense that the sun is shining in the middle of the night.

Day 3

Skills Practiced

Use of quotation marks with title of a poem.

Correction of sentence fragment.

Capitalization of name of geographic area.

Practice Sentences

1. Byrd Baylor wrote many poems including <u>When Clay Sings</u>. Finding clay pots and imagining the lives of the people who made them.

2. Tom Bahti, who uses designs of the southwest, illustrated the poem.

Answers

1. Byrd Baylor wrote many poems including "When Clay Sings." This poem is about finding clay pots and imagining the lives of the people who made them.

2. Tom Bahti, who uses designs of the Southwest, illustrated the poem.

Day 4

Skills Practiced

Use of commas with nonrestrictive clause.

Correction of faulty parallel structure.

Practice Sentences

1. Broken pieces of clay which come in many sizes and shapes can be gathered and fit together like the pieces of a puzzle.
2. To make the bowls, potters shape, polish, bake, and are painting designs.

Answers

1. Broken pieces of clay, which come in many sizes and shapes, can be gathered and fit together like the pieces of a puzzle.
2. To make the bowls, potters shape, polish, bake, and paint designs.

Day 5

Skills Practiced

Combining sentences.

Use of comma after introductory prepositional phrase.

Use of hyphen with the prefix *all*.

Practice Sentences

1. In his poem "Alone in the Nets," Arnold Adoff uses the placement of letters to help get across his ideas. He places the letters with care.
2. Under pressure at the net the narrator seems to be losing interest in the all American sport of soccer.

Answers

1. In his poem "Alone in the Nets," Arnold Adoff carefully places the letters to help get across his ideas.
2. Under pressure at the net, the narrator seems to be losing interest in the all-American sport of soccer.

Day 1

Skills Practiced

Correct capitalization of name of season.

Correct use of apostrophe to show possession.

Use of comma after introductory prepositional phrases.

Practice Sentences

1. The reader hears the sound of a Spring rain from the poets point of view in the poem "April Rain Song" by Langston Hughes.
2. In her poem about the sky Ms. Silko paints a picture of an endless sky.

Answers

1. The reader hears the sound of a spring rain from the poet's point of view in the poem "April Rain Song" by Langston Hughes.
2. In her poem about the sky, Ms. Silko paints a picture of an endless sky.

Day 2

Skills Practiced

Use of underlining or italics with words used as words.

Use of separate sentences to revise stringy sentence.

Use of quotation marks with title of a poem.

Use of commas with interrupter.

Practice Sentences

1. A simile points out a similar quality between two things and uses the words like or as and similes are often used by poets in their writing.
2. In the poem Sun by Valerie Worth for example the poet compares the yellow patches of sun on the floor to a quilt.

Answers

1. A simile points out a similar quality between two things and uses the words <u>like</u> or <u>as</u>. Similes are often used by poets in their writing.
2. In the poem "Sun" by Valerie Worth, for example, the poet compares the yellow patches of sun on the floor to a quilt.

Day 3

Skills Practiced

Use of comma with coordinate adjectives.

Use of quotation marks to show a speaker's exact words.

Correct pronoun case in compound construction.

Practice Sentences

1. Clouds can create fun fanciful characters that often capture a writer's imagination.
2. Me and my brother Leon love to look at clouds and find shapes in them, Todd told the class.

Answers

1. Clouds can create fun, fanciful characters that often capture a writer's imagination.
2. "My brother Leon and I love to look at clouds and find shapes in them," Todd told the class.

Day 4

Skills Practiced

Elimination of unnecessary colon.

Use of semicolons in a series containing commas.

Use of comma after introductory phrase.

Practice Sentences

1. The three main types of clouds are: cumulus clouds, which are the big, fluffy clouds, stratus clouds, which are the low, layer clouds, and cirrus clouds, which are thin, wispy clouds.

2. When writing about the sky poets are usually more concerned about imagery than terminology.

Answers

1. The three main types of clouds are cumulus clouds, which are the big, fluffy clouds; stratus clouds, which are the low, layer clouds; and cirrus clouds, which are thin, wispy clouds.

2. When writing about the sky, poets are usually more concerned about imagery than terminology.

Day 5

Skills Practiced

Combining sentences.

Correct use of semicolon and comma with a conjunctive adverb.

Practice Sentences

1. Nimby is a book. Nimby is by Jasper Tomkins. It is the story of an unusual cloud.

2. Nimby is more than a story about a cloud that can change shape, in fact; it is a story about being an individual.

Answers

1. Nimby, a book by Jasper Tomkins, is the story of an unusual cloud.

2. Nimby is more than a story about a cloud that can change shape; in fact, it is a story about being an individual.

Daily Language Practice • Week 28

Day 1

Skills Practiced

Subject and verb agreement.

Use of commas with nonrestrictive clause.

Correct placement of question mark with quotation marks.

Practice Sentences

1. George Shannon's <u>Stories to Solve</u> are a collection of folk tales which are also puzzles from around the world.

2. What does Mr. Shannon mean in his statement "When I am telling stories, I am writing out loud as I go so that each telling is fresh . . . ?"

Answers

1. George Shannon's <u>Stories to Solve</u> is a collection of folk tales, which are also puzzles, from around the world.

2. What does Mr. Shannon mean in his statement "When I am telling stories, I am writing out loud as I go so that each telling is fresh . . . "?

Day 2

Skills Practiced

Elimination of double comparison.

Pronoun agreement with antecedent.

Practice Sentences

1. In one folk-tale puzzle, the father tells his three sons that he will give his property to the one who proves to be the most cleverest son.

2. The father gives each son a coin and challenges them to buy something to fill a room completely.

Answers

1. In one folk-tale puzzle, the father tells his three sons that he will give his property to the one who proves to be the most clever son.

2. The father gives each son a coin and challenges him to buy something to fill a room completely.

Day 3

Skills Practiced

Combining sentences.

Correct contraction with helping verb *have*.

Correction of misplaced modifier.

Practice Sentences

1. Miriam likes reading puzzles. Miriam likes writing puzzles. She likes solving them, too.

2. When she went to the library, Miriam would of taken out several books with folk-tale puzzles, but she could only find one.

Answers

1. Miriam likes reading, writing, and solving puzzles.

2. When she went to the library, Miriam would've taken out several books with folk-tale puzzles, but she could find only one.

Day 4

Skills Practiced

Correct punctuation of split quotation.

Correct pronoun case.

Correction of sentence fragment.

Practice Sentences

1. "Do you know the answer to the puzzle?" the teacher asked. "or should I give you a clue?"

2. Knowing the answer is safe with Alonzo and I, the teacher handed us a sealed envelope. Before he left the room.

Answers

1. "Do you know the answer to the puzzle," the teacher asked, "or should I give you a clue?"

2. Knowing the answer is safe with Alonzo and me, the teacher handed us a sealed envelope before he left the room.

Day 5

Skills Practiced

Use of comma before a coordinating conjunction in a compound sentence.

Capitalization of proper adjective.

Spelling out numbers through one hundred.

Elimination of faulty parallel structure.

Practice Sentences

1. A well-known math puzzle called "Dividing the Horses" is of unknown origin but similar tales can be found in Jewish literature and eurasian folk tales.

2. In this puzzle 17 horses are to be divided among a farmer's sons in the following way: one-half to his eldest son, one-third to his middle son, and his youngest son gets one-ninth.

Answers

1. A well-known math puzzle called "Dividing the Horses" is of unknown origin, but similar tales can be found in Jewish literature and Eurasian folk tales.

2. In this puzzle seventeen horses are to be divided among a farmer's sons in the following way: one-half to his eldest son, one-third to his middle son, and one-ninth to his youngest son.

Day 1

Skills Practiced

Use of comma after introductory prepositional phrase.

Subject and verb agreement.

Revision of sentence ending with a preposition.

Use of question mark with quotation marks.

Practice Sentences

1. In the story "Señor Coyote and the Tricked Trickster" each of the characters are a trickster.

2. "What story about a trickster can you think of," asked the storyteller.

Answers

1. In the story "Señor Coyote and the Tricked Trickster," each of the characters is a trickster.

2. "What story do you know about a trickster?" asked the storyteller.

Day 2

Skills Practiced

Use of semicolon to correct run-on sentence.

Use of comma after introductory prepositional phrases.

Elimination of unnecessary comma with adverb clause.

Practice Sentences

1. Sometimes folk tales are similar to one another "The Lion and the Mouse" is basically the same story as "Señor Coyote and the Tricked Trickster."

2. In both of these folk tales the mouse chews through a rope, so that the larger animal can go free.

Answers

1. Sometimes folk tales are similar to one another; "The Lion and the Mouse" is basically the same story as "Señor Coyote and the Tricked Trickster."

2. In both of these folk tales, the mouse chews through a rope so that the larger animal can go free.

Day 3

Skills Practiced

Use of apostrophe in a contraction.

Elimination of comma with a restrictive appositive.

Correct subordinating conjunction *so that*.

Practice Sentences

1. Its very amusing to see how the fox tricks the gingerbread boy in the folk tale, "The Gingerbread Boy."

2. The fox gains the gingerbread boy's trust so he can eat the boy.

Answers

1. It's very amusing to see how the fox tricks the boy in the folk tale "The Gingerbread Boy."

2. The fox gains the gingerbread boy's trust so that he can eat the boy.

Day 4

Skills Practiced

Correct contraction with helping verb *have*.

Use of coordinating conjunction to combine sentences.

Correction of *they* without a clear antecedent.

Practice Sentences

1. In the African folk tale "Why Monkeys Live in Trees," the monkey would of won the gold. The lion saw the trick the monkey was playing.
2. When the leopard realized they had all been tricked, he leaped into the tall grass where the monkeys were hiding.

Answers

1. In the African folk tale "Why Monkeys Live in Trees," the monkey would've won the gold, but the lion saw the trick the monkey was playing.
2. When the leopard realized all the animals had been tricked, he leaped into the tall grass where the monkeys were hiding.

Day 5

Skills Practiced

Revision of wordy sentence.

Correct indefinite article.

Elimination of hyphen used with compound modifier.

Practice Sentences

1. What I want to say is that the trickster, a favorite character in many folk tales, is often a animal.
2. The trickster's beautifully-crafted plans rely on wit and intelligence rather than on physical strength.

Answers

1. The trickster, a favorite character in many folk tales, is often an animal.
2. The trickster's beautifully crafted plans rely on wit and intelligence rather than on physical strength.

Daily Language Practice • Week 30

Day 1

Skills Practiced

Combining sentences.

Subject and verb agreement.

Correction of sentence fragment.

Practice Sentences

1. Folk tales are an old form of literature. Myths are an old form of literature. Legends are an old form of literature.

2. Many stories from these types of literature is rooted in oral tradition. The telling of stories over and over again from one generation to the next.

Answers

1. Folk tales, myths, and legends are old forms of literature.

2. Many stories from this type of literature are rooted in oral tradition, which is the telling of stories over and over again from one generation to the next.

Day 2

Skills Practiced

Capitalization of proper adjective.

Capitalization of first word of quotation.

Inclusion of closing quotation marks.

Practice Sentences

1. Knots on a Counting Rope explains how a young native american boy learns a story to carry on the oral tradition.

2. Grandfather tells the boy, "by the time this rope is full of knots, you will know the story by heart.

Answers

1. Knots on a Counting Rope explains how a young Native American boy learns a story to carry on the oral tradition.

2. Grandfather tells the boy, "By the time this rope is full of knots, you will know the story by heart."

Day 3

Skills Practiced

Use of apostrophe to show joint possession.

Use of hyphen in compound noun.

Use of comma after introductory subordinate clause.

Practice Sentences

1. Elena and Tomas great grandfather is a respected storyteller in their town.

2. As soon as the storyteller finished the story the crowd burst into applause.

Answers

1. Elena and Tomas's great-grandfather is a respected storyteller in their town.

2. As soon as the storyteller finished the story, the crowd burst into applause.

Day 4

Skills Practiced

Use of comma with nonrestrictive clause.

Correct past form of irregular verb.

Subject and verb agreement.

Practice Sentences

1. The oral tradition continues through such events as the National Storytelling Festival which begun in the early 1970's.

2. A collection of stories have been compiled in a book titled <u>Best-Loved Stories Told at the National Storytelling Festival</u>.

Answers

1. The oral tradition continues through such events as the National Storytelling Festival, which began in the early 1970's.

2. A collection of stories has been compiled in a book titled <u>Best-Loved Stories Told at the National Storytelling Festival</u>.

Day 5

Skills Practiced

Use of subordinating conjunction to combine sentences.

Correction of faulty parallel structure.

Use of apostrophe to show omitted letter.

Eliminating *here* and *there* after a demonstrative adjective.

Practice Sentences

1. It is fun to read these stories. Listening to them is more fun.

2. After reading the brochure, Smitty emphatically stated, "I'm aimin to go to that there festival this fall."

Answers

1. While it is fun to read these stories, it is more fun to listen to them.

2. After reading the brochure, Smitty emphatically stated, "I'm aimin' to go to that festival this fall."

Daily Language Practice • Week 31

Day 1

Skills Practiced

Use of relative clause to combine sentences.

Correction of commonly confused words.

Revision of wordy sentence.

Practice Sentences

1. Legends are stories about the past. Every culture has it's legends.
2. What legends are are stories that help readers understand the traditions and beliefs of a people.

Answers

1. Every culture has its legends, which are stories about the past.
2. Legends are stories that help readers understand the traditions and beliefs of a people.

Day 2

Skills Practiced

Correct spelling of homophones.

Subject and verb agreement.

Use of comma and subordinating conjunction to combine sentences.

Practice Sentences

1. King Arthur, as well as his nights, are the subject of many fascinating legends.
2. Legends may or may not be founded on fact. It is doubtful King Arthur would recognize stories told about him today.

Answers

1. King Arthur, as well as his knights, is the subject of many fascinating legends.
2. Since legends may or may not be founded on fact, it is doubtful that King Arthur would recognize stories told about him today.

Day 3

Skills Practiced

Use of separate sentences to correct run-on sentence.

Revision of sentence ending with a preposition.

Elimination of comma in compound predicate.

Capitalization of important words in title.

Practice Sentences

1. The dream catcher is an old Ojibwa tradition, there is a story, or legend, that it goes with.
2. Karen Hartman retells the story, and provides additional information about dream catchers in her book <u>Dream Catcher: The legend and the lady</u>.

Answers

1. The dream catcher is an old Ojibwa tradition. There is a story, or legend, that goes with it.
2. Karen Hartman retells the story and provides additional information about dream catchers in her book <u>Dream Catcher: The Legend and the Lady</u>.

Day 4	**Skills Practiced**	**Practice Sentences**
	Subject and verb agreement.	1. Often, the beads on a dream catcher is red yellow black and white.
	Use of comma in a series.	2. The feather on a dream catcher lets each good dream slide down so it can tickle the sleeper.
	Correct subordinating conjunction *so that*.	**Answers**
		1. Often, the beads on a dream catcher are red, yellow, black, and white.
		2. The feather on a dream catcher lets each good dream slide down so that it can tickle the sleeper.

Day 5	**Skills Practiced**	**Practice Sentences**
	Correct contraction with helping verb *have*.	1. In <u>The Legend of the Bluebonnet</u>, the young girl could of turned her back on her people; she made a great sacrifice to help them.
	Use of conjunctive adverb.	2. After reading the story about the bluebonnet the state flower of Texas, Myra said, "I like this story because it is good."
	Use of parentheses to set off information.	**Answers**
	Revision of empty sentence.	1. In <u>The Legend of the Bluebonnet</u>, the young girl could've turned her back on her people; instead, she made a great sacrifice to help them.
		2. After reading the story about the bluebonnet (the state flower of Texas), Myra said, "I like this story because it tells about my favorite flower, the bluebonnet."

Day 1

Skills Practiced

Use of commas to set off appositive.

Use of numerals and words for round numbers ending in millions.

Use of adverb to modify adjective.

Practice Sentences

1. The sun our closest star is 93,000,000 miles from Earth.
2. Did you know that ancient Greek astronomers were real accurate in measuring the distance to the sun?

Answers

1. The sun, our closest star, is 93 million miles from Earth.
2. Did you know that ancient Greek astronomers were really accurate in measuring the distance to the sun?

Day 2

Skills Practiced

Revision of wordy sentence.

Correction of commonly confused words.

Use of commas to set off appositive.

Practice Sentences

1. What I want to say is that long ago people used there imaginations to see people and animal shapes in the stars.
2. Myths stories about the earth, the moon, and the sky help explain events in nature.

Answers

1. Long ago people used their imaginations to see people and animal shapes in the stars.
2. Myths, stories about the earth, the moon, and the sky help explain events in nature.

Day 3

Skills Practiced

Subject and verb agreement.

Correction of sentence fragment.

Use of conjunctive adverb to combine sentences.

Practice Sentences

1. One of the myths are about Orion. Who bragged he could slay all the animals on Earth.
2. Scorpius was sent to Earth to stop this from happening. A great fight broke out between Scorpius and Orion.

Answers

1. One of the myths is about Orion, who bragged he could slay all the animals on Earth.
2. Scorpius was sent to Earth to stop this from happening; as a result, a great fight broke out between Scorpius and Orion.

Day 4

Skills Practiced

Use of commas with interrupters.

Use of definite article.

Use of end punctuation: question mark.

Practice Sentences

1. What pictures if any do you see in the sky?
2. Can you find a North Star (Polaris), which is part of the constellation called Ursa Minor.

Answers

1. What pictures, if any, do you see in the sky?
2. Can you find the North Star (Polaris), which is part of the constellation called Ursa Minor?

Day 5

Skills Practiced

Correct capitalization of name of a direction.

Capitalization of proper noun.

Correct capitalization in a split quotation.

Practice Sentences

1. "When I look at the Northern night sky, I have trouble finding the north star," complained Patrick.
2. "Well," suggested the astronomer, "Use the Big Dipper to help you find the north star in the handle of the Little Dipper."

Answers

1. "When I look at the northern night sky, I have trouble finding the North Star," complained Patrick.
2. "Well," suggested the astronomer, "use the Big Dipper to help you find the North Star in the handle of the Little Dipper."

Day 1

Skills Practiced

Use of comma to set off direct quotation.

Inclusion of closing quotation marks.

Correction of sentence fragment.

Practice Sentences

1. The teacher said "We are going to read Greek myths this month.

2. Greek myths are stories about Greek gods. Stories about heroes and monsters.

Answers

1. The teacher said, "We are going to read Greek myths this month."

2. Greek myths are stories about Greek gods, heroes, and monsters.

Day 2

Skills Practiced

Elimination of unnecessary comma before subordinate clause.

Correction of unclear pronoun antecedent.

Use of vivid verb to improve style.

Use of exclamation point after interjection.

Practice Sentences

1. In Greek mythology, the goddess Athene changes Medusa's hair into snakes, because she says that her hair is more beautiful than Athene's.

2. "Wow. That's what I'd call a really bad hair day," joked Myrna.

Answers

1. In Greek mythology, the goddess Athene changes Medusa's hair into snakes because Medusa brags that her hair is more beautiful than Athene's.

2. "Wow! That's what I'd call a really bad hair day," joked Myrna.

Day 3

Skills Practiced

Revision of sentence ending with preposition.

Subject and verb agreement.

Use of adverb to modify adjective.

Practice Sentences

1. Alonzo gave a report on Greek myths he had read about.

2. "I thought the story about Phaëthon and his ride in the chariot of the sun god were real good," Alonzo said.

Answers

1. Alonzo gave a report about Greek myths he had read.

2. "I thought the story about Phaëthon and his ride in the chariot of the sun god was really good," Alonzo said.

Day 4

Skills Practiced

- Use of comma after introductory prepositional phrases.
- Correction of commonly confused words.
- Use of hyphen in a compound noun.

Practice Sentences

1. In the myth about the golden apples theirs a great race between Atalanta and Hippomenes.
2. Hippomenes, the great grandson of Neptune, was confident that he could win the race.

Answers

1. In the myth about the golden apples, there's a great race between Atalanta and Hippomenes.
2. Hippomenes, the great-grandson of Neptune, was confident that he could win the race.

Day 5

Skills Practiced

- Formation of irregular verb tense.
- Use of semicolon and conjunctive adverb to combine sentences.
- Use of comma after introductory phrase.
- Correct pronoun case.

Practice Sentences

1. During the race, Hippomenes throwed a golden apple in Atalanta's path. She slowed down.
2. After reading the story about Atalanta I wondered if I could run as fast as her.

Answers

1. During the race, Hippomenes threw a golden apple in Atalanta's path; consequently, she slowed down.
2. After reading the story about Atalanta, I wondered if I could run as fast as she.

Daily Language Practice • Week 34

Day 1

Skills Practiced

Use of semicolon and conjunctive adverb to combine sentences.

Use of underlining or italics for words used as words.

Subject and verb agreement.

Practice Sentences

1. Many English words have Greek origins. Arachnid is the scientific term for the spider family.

2. A Greek myth about Arachne and Athene give insight into the origin of this term.

Answers

1. Many English words have Greek origins; for example, <u>arachnid</u> is the scientific term for the spider family.

2. A Greek myth about Arachne and Athene gives insight into the origin of this term.

Day 2

Skills Practiced

Revision of wordy sentence.

Use of comma after introductory subordinate clause.

Use of hyphen in compound modifier.

Use of vivid verb to improve style.

Practice Sentences

1. Something I am wondering is if you are familiar with the myth about Arachne.

2. As the story goes Arachne, a well known weaver, says that she is a better weaver than the goddess Athene.

Answers

1. Are you familiar with the myth about Arachne?

2. As the story goes, Arachne, a well-known weaver, boasts that she is a better weaver than the goddess Athene.

Day 3

Skills Practiced

Use of subordinating conjunction to combine sentences.

Correction of pronoun shift.

Correction of sentence fragment.

Practice Sentences

1. Arachne does not heed the warning to ask Athene's forgiveness. The weaving contest begins.

2. Arachne chooses many different colors because she knows you must vary your threads. To keep the design interesting.

Answers

1. When Arachne does not heed the warning to ask Athene's forgiveness, the weaving contest begins.

2. Arachne chooses many different colors because she knows she must vary her threads to keep the design interesting.

Day 4

Skills Practiced

Use of comma before coordinating conjunction in a compound sentence.

Use of quotation marks to show a speaker's exact words.

Use of precise adjective to improve style.

Practice Sentences

1. Athene gives one last warning to Arachne but Arachne weaves scenes that show how the gods have hurt humans.

2. Here the storyteller paused and asked, What do you think will happen to Arachne for weaving such bad scenes?

Answers

1. Athene gives one last warning to Arachne, but Arachne weaves scenes that show how the gods have hurt humans.

2. Here the storyteller paused and asked, "What do you think will happen to Arachne for weaving such wicked scenes?"

Day 5

Skills Practiced

Correct spelling of homophones.

Use of comma with a split quotation.

Use of adverb to modify verb.

Practice Sentences

1. "Now that I have herd the story of Arachne," Jerome said. "I will think twice before I brag about how good I am."

2. "Spiders weave really good," added Ana.

Answers

1. "Now that I have heard the story of Arachne," Jerome said, "I will think twice before I brag about how good I am."

2. "Spiders weave really well," added Ana.

Day 1

Skills Practiced

Correct use of indefinite article.

Revision of choppy sentences.

Spelling out name of state in prose.

Use of commas with interrupter.

Practice Sentences

1. Mildred D. Taylor is a author. She writes books. Her books are for young people.

2. Born in Jackson, MS, Ms. Taylor along with her family later moved north.

Answers

1. Mildred D. Taylor, an author, writes books for young people.

2. Born in Jackson, Mississippi, Ms. Taylor, along with her family, later moved north.

Day 2

Skills Practiced

Revision of wordy sentence.

Use of active voice to improve style.

Use of relative clause to combine sentences.

Use of comma around nonrestrictive clause.

Practice Sentences

1. The book Song of the Trees was the book that started Ms. Taylor's writing career. This book was given an award because it was named the Winner of the 1973 Council on Interracial Books Award.

2. Based on a true story, this book is about the Logan family who owns land, and some men who try to cheat the Logans out of their land.

Answers

1. Ms. Taylor's writing career began with the book Song of the Trees, which won the 1973 Council on Interracial Books Award.

2. Based on a true story, this book is about the Logan family, who owns land, and some men who try to cheat the Logans out of their land.

Day 3

Skills Practiced

Use of apostrophe with amount of money that modifies a noun.

Correction of faulty subordination.

Use of hyphen with the prefix self-.

Practice Sentences

1. In a commanding voice, Mr. Andersen asks Big Ma to let him cut down sixty-five dollars worth of trees.

2. Because he saves the trees that are left and keeps his self respect, David confronts Mr. Andersen.

Answers

1. In a commanding voice, Mr. Andersen asks Big Ma to let him cut down sixty-five dollars' worth of trees.

2. Because he confronts Mr. Andersen, David saves the trees that are left and keeps his self-respect.

Day 4

Skills Practiced

Use of apostrophe to show possession.

Subject and verb agreement.

Use of subordinating conjunction to combine sentences.

Use of quotation marks to show a speaker's exact words.

Practice Sentences

1. Each of Mildred D. Taylors books are based on family stories.

2. Ms. Taylor's father died. Ms. Taylor said, My father was my greatest inspiration for writing.

Answers

1. Each of Mildred D. Taylor's books is based on family stories.

2. When her father died, Ms. Taylor said, "My father was my greatest inspiration for writing."

Day 5

Skills Practiced

Revision of empty sentence.

Use of commas in a series.

Elimination of faulty parallel structure.

Practice Sentences

1. Sam's favorite book by Ms. Taylor is Mississippi Bridge because he likes it.

2. Like Ms. Taylor's family, my family likes reading stories telling stories and having someone tell stories to us.

Answers

1. Sam's favorite book by Ms. Taylor is Mississippi Bridge because it makes him think about the right and the wrong way to treat people.

2. Like Ms. Taylor's family, my family likes reading stories, telling stories, and listening to others tell stories.

Day 1

Skills Practiced

Use of exclamation point to show strong emotion.

Revision of choppy sentences.

Subject and verb agreement.

Practice Sentences

1. "I just finished reading <u>Tuck Everlasting</u>. What a fantastic book it is," exclaimed Jane.

2. The Tuck family has a secret. No one else must discover it. One little girl do.

Answers

1. "I just finished reading <u>Tuck Everlasting</u>. What a fantastic book it is!" exclaimed Jane.

2. The Tuck family has a secret that no one else must discover, but one little girl does.

Day 2

Skills Practiced

Use of appositive to combine sentences.

Use of adjective to add specific detail.

Correction of misplaced modifier.

Practice Sentences

1. Winnie Foster is one of the main characters in <u>Tuck Everlasting</u>. She has to make many decisions.

2. It is hard to believe she only is ten years old.

Answers

1. Winnie Foster, one of the main characters in <u>Tuck Everlasting</u>, has to make many difficult decisions.

2. It is hard to believe she is only ten years old.

Day 3

Skills Practiced

Subject and verb agreement.

Use of subordinating conjunction to combine sentences.

Use of comma before coordinating conjunction in a compound sentence.

Correct placement of question mark with quotation marks.

Practice Sentences

1. Neither the Fosters nor the constable are convinced that Winnie went with the Tucks. She wanted to go.

2. "Was Winnie kidnapped or did she go of her own free will"? the teacher asked.

Answers

1. Neither the Fosters nor the constable is convinced that Winnie went with the Tucks because she wanted to go.

2. "Was Winnie kidnapped, or did she go of her own free will?" the teacher asked.

Day 4

Skills Practiced

Use of end punctuation: question mark.

Use of comma as part of greeting in a personal letter.

Correction of commonly confused words.

Practice Sentences

1. Do you think Winnie Foster ever wanted to write Jesse Tuck after he had left.

2. One of her letters might have read like this:

   Dear Jesse

   Today, I set outside and watched a toad on the road. . . .

Answers

1. Do you think Winnie Foster ever wanted to write Jesse Tuck after he had left?

2. One of her letters might have read like this:

   Dear Jesse,

   Today, I sat outside and watched a toad on the road. . . .

Day 5

Skills Practiced

Correction of faulty subordination.

Correct contraction with helping verb *have*.

Elimination of unnecessary comma before subordinating clause.

Practice Sentences

1. Because they would live forever, the Tuck family sipped water from the underground spring.

2. Do you think the Tuck family would of taken a drink from the spring, if they had known the consequences?

Answers

1. Because they sipped water from the underground spring, the Tuck family would live forever.

2. Do you think the Tuck family would've taken a drink from the spring if they had known the consequences?